THE CREATION

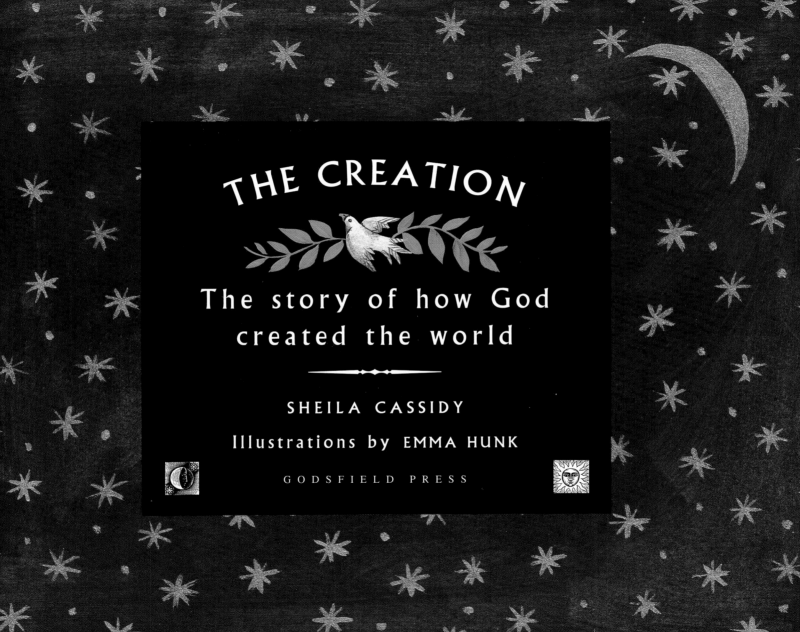

THE CREATION

The story of how God created the world

SHEILA CASSIDY

Illustrations by EMMA HUNK

GODSFIELD PRESS

In the very beginning God created the Heavens and the Earth. All he had was a lump of clay and a ball of wool. "What shall I make of this clay?" he said. "How can I free its spirit? What shall I knit from this ball of yarn?"

God took the clay and very carefully rolled it out like dough. When it was paper thin, God cut it into strips, like spaghetti, and hung it out to dry.

When the strips were nearly dry, God began to knit them together, and little by little something amazing began to take shape.

When the spaghetti mud ran out, God looked around for something else to knit with. After a while, she saw some blue hydrogen atoms and some white oxygen atoms floating by and she caught them in her butterfly net. Then, very carefully, she spun them together into a fine, soft yarn, a bit like Angora.

Then, changing her knitting needles for a single, great needle, God knit the blue yarn onto the brown clay to make a big, round ball.

When she had finished, God named the
blue bit THE HEAVENS and the brown
part she named THE EARTH. She sat
back and admired her work, and then
she went to bed.

⭐ *It was the end of the first day.*

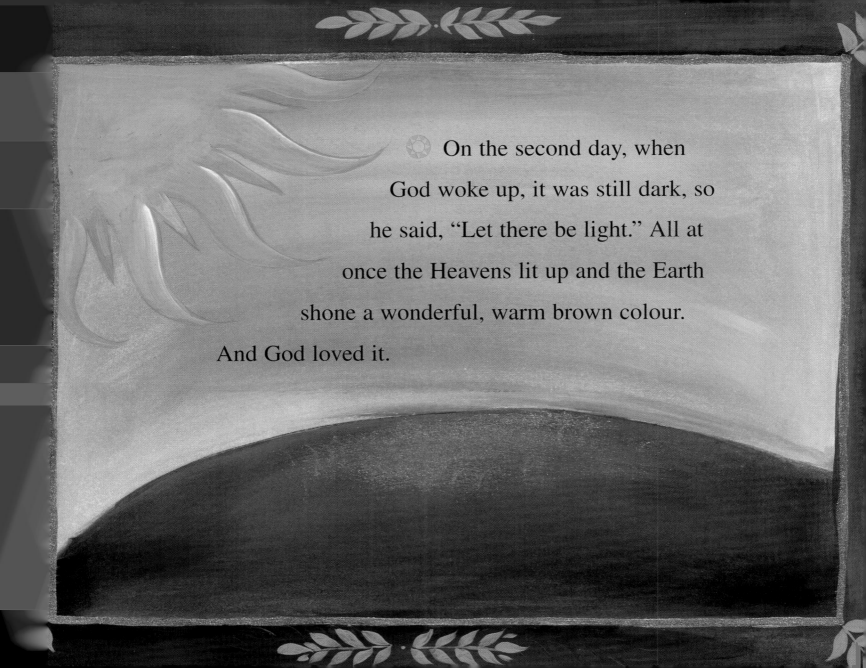

On the second day, when God woke up, it was still dark, so he said, "Let there be light." All at once the Heavens lit up and the Earth shone a wonderful, warm brown colour. And God loved it.

Because he loved the good, brown Earth, God blessed it and made it fertile. Green buds appeared, grass and plants of every kind. Tall trees grew, fruit bushes and flowers of every colour. Each plant had its own seeds so that in due time the whole Earth might blossom.

When God
saw what he had made he
was really thrilled! He smiled to himself
and went to bed.

It was the end of the second day.

On that second night, God was so
excited that she could not sleep, so she got up
again and went to see how her garden was growing.
The night was so dark that she could not see, so she said,
"Let there be some very gentle lights for the night."
And lo! There appeared a whole galaxy of twinkling stars
and the first new moon. God sat under a tree
just watching the stars, and after a while
she fell asleep.

When she woke up it was morning and
all the stars had vanished. God felt sad because
the sky looked empty.
After a while, God chuckled and said, "Let there
be creatures to enjoy the sky, feathered creatures
great and small." And so it was.

God had so much fun making the birds that he burst
into song. Astonished, the birds listened to him, and then, one
by one, they answered him with their own
song. God laughed and laughed in sheer joy,
and then, exhausted, he went to bed.

It was the end of the third day.

On the fourth day,

God was full of joy and energy.

Humming a little song, he returned to his

clay and began to play.

He worked quickly and
skilfully, fashioning a multitude of creatures,
great and small. By nightfall, the Earth was full
of animals, running about, leaping and snorting
with delight.

Night fell and all the animals went to sleep (except those that God had created for the hours of darkness). God looked at his sleeping creatures, and loved them.

Then, weary himself, God lay down under the stars and went to sleep. ⭐ *It was the end of the fourth day.*

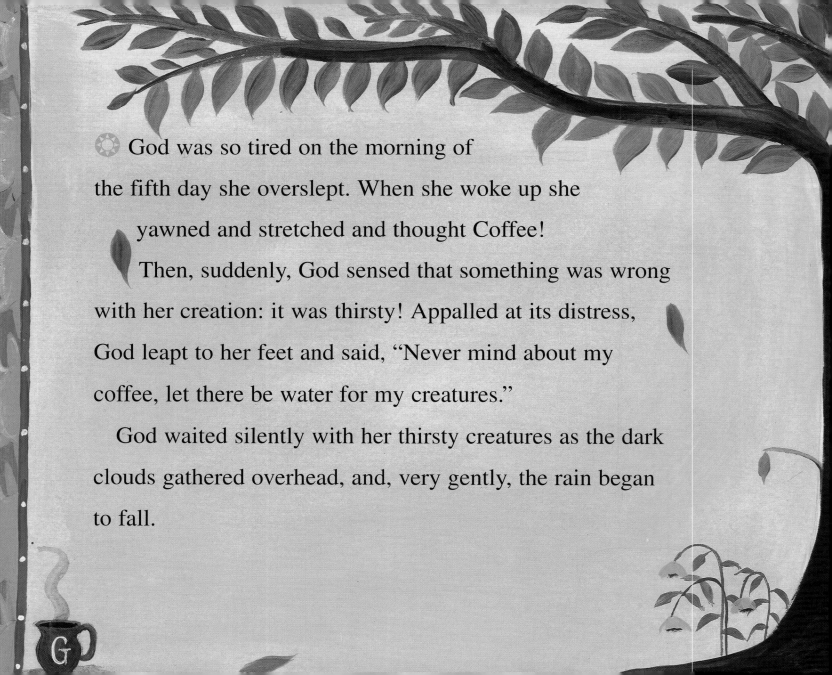

God was so tired on the morning of
the fifth day she overslept. When she woke up she
     yawned and stretched and thought Coffee!
     Then, suddenly, God sensed that something was wrong
with her creation: it was thirsty! Appalled at its distress,
God leapt to her feet and said, "Never mind about my
coffee, let there be water for my creatures."
     God waited silently with her thirsty creatures as the dark
clouds gathered overhead, and, very gently, the rain began
to fall.

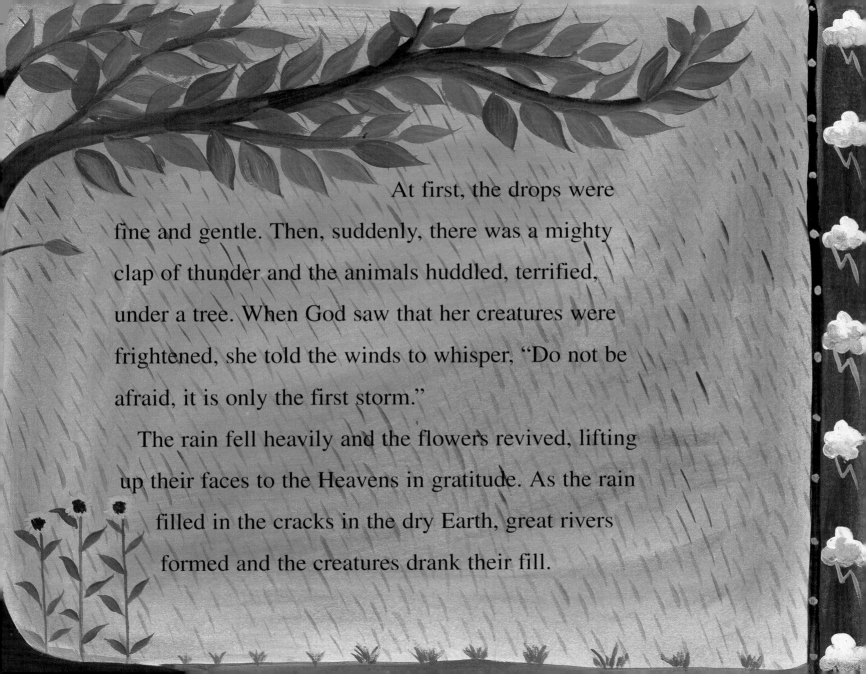

At first, the drops were
fine and gentle. Then, suddenly, there was a mighty
clap of thunder and the animals huddled, terrified,
under a tree. When God saw that her creatures were
frightened, she told the winds to whisper, "Do not be
afraid, it is only the first storm."

The rain fell heavily and the flowers revived, lifting
up their faces to the Heavens in gratitude. As the rain
filled in the cracks in the dry Earth, great rivers
formed and the creatures drank their fill.

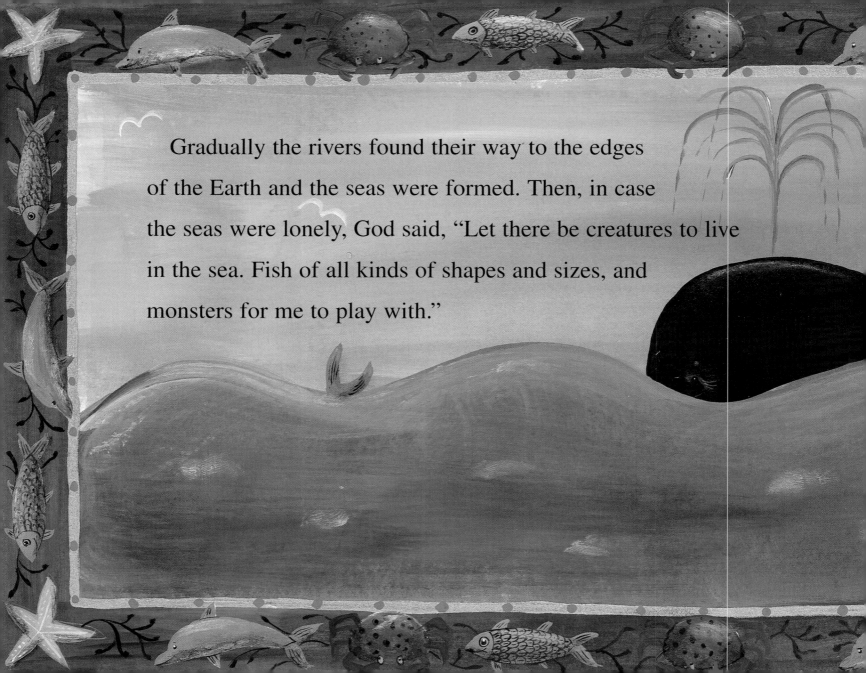

Gradually the rivers found their way to the edges of the Earth and the seas were formed. Then, in case the seas were lonely, God said, "Let there be creatures to live in the sea. Fish of all kinds of shapes and sizes, and monsters for me to play with."

God spent so long playing in the water that he got very cold and wet, so he went home and had a hot bath and went to bed and slept.

⭐ *It was the end of the fifth day.*

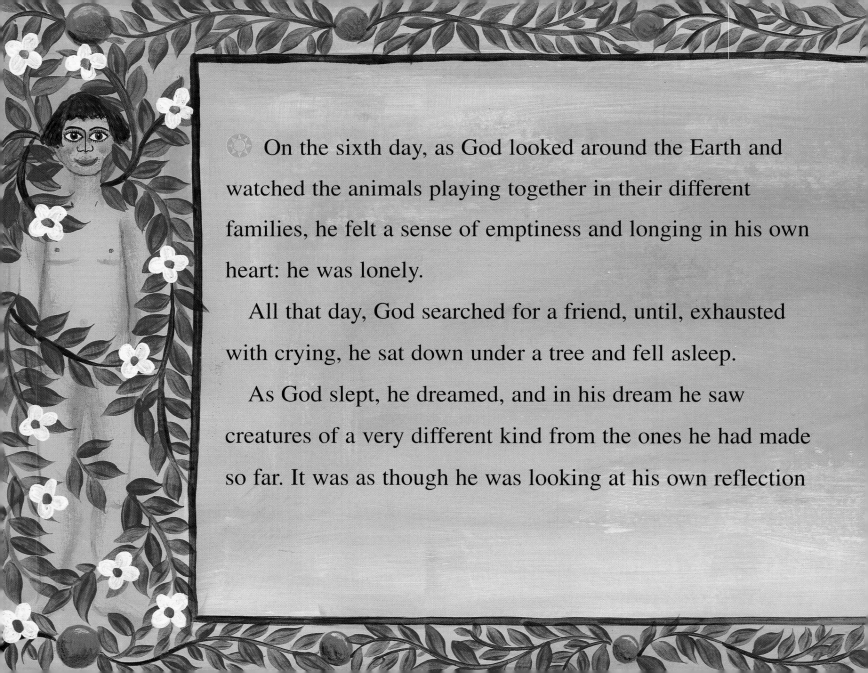

On the sixth day, as God looked around the Earth and watched the animals playing together in their different families, he felt a sense of emptiness and longing in his own heart: he was lonely.

All that day, God searched for a friend, until, exhausted with crying, he sat down under a tree and fell asleep.

As God slept, he dreamed, and in his dream he saw creatures of a very different kind from the ones he had made so far. It was as though he was looking at his own reflection in one of the still mountain lakes, except that there were many of these reflections, not just one.

When she woke, God knew what she had to do. Taking her basket of wools, she went down to the lakeside and began to knit. She knitted as fast as she could lest she forget the images of the dream, and before long there stood two beautiful creatures of amazing beauty, thinking, talking, dreaming people, just like herself.

Excitedly, God embraced her new creatures and arm in arm the three of them walked around the garden. "Look," said God. "Isn't it wonderful! This is an orange, a parrot, a mouse, a daisy!"

Then God made them welcome, with a rare feast of bread and honey, olives and nuts and a wonderful bowl of fruit. As they ate, God told them of his plans for the world and they listened intently, sharing his excitement and joy.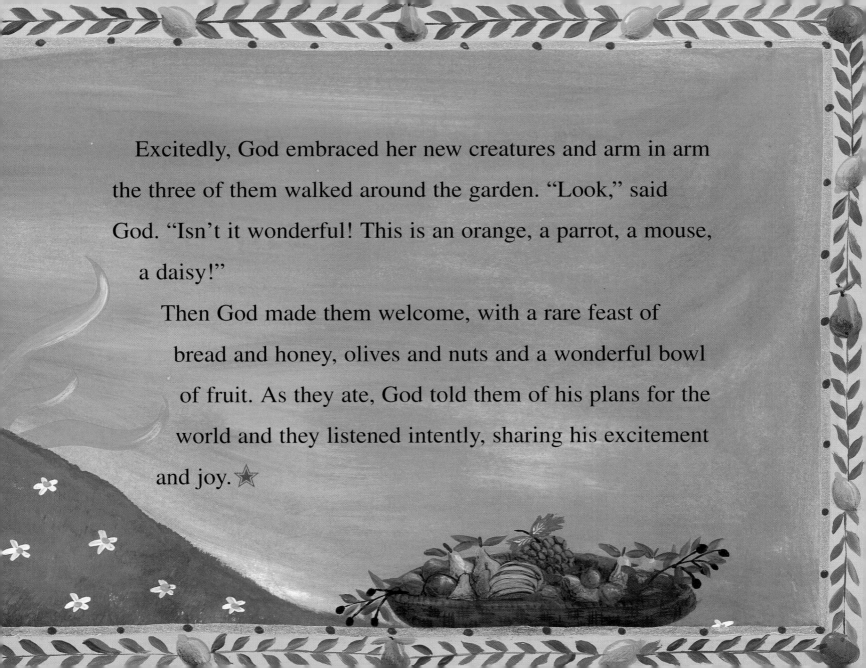

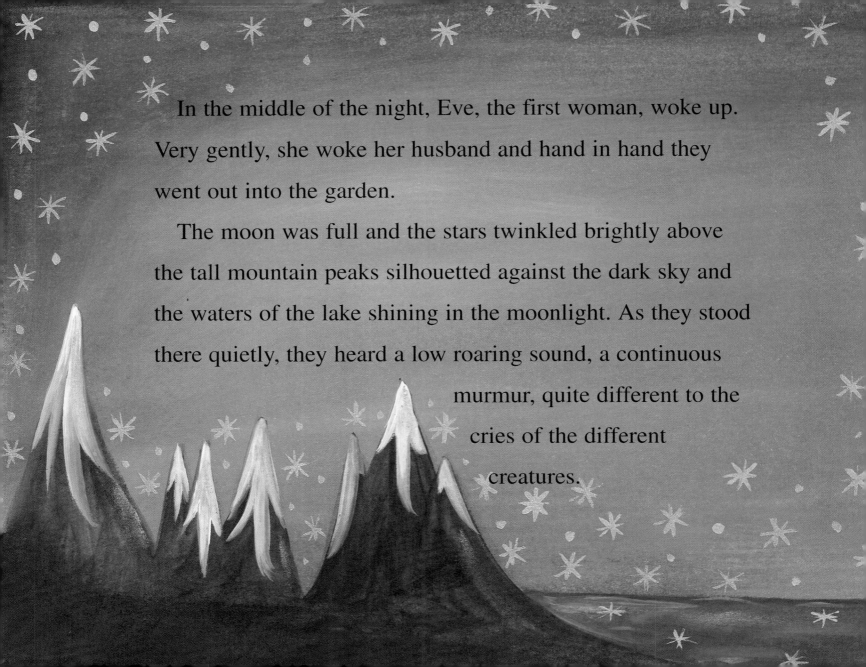

In the middle of the night, Eve, the first woman, woke up. Very gently, she woke her husband and hand in hand they went out into the garden.

The moon was full and the stars twinkled brightly above the tall mountain peaks silhouetted against the dark sky and the waters of the lake shining in the moonlight. As they stood there quietly, they heard a low roaring sound, a continuous murmur, quite different to the cries of the different creatures.

"Let's go and see," said Eve. So hand in hand they walked in the moonlight until gradually the sound became a roar, and there stretched out before them as far as the eye could see was the ocean.

For a while they stood spellbound, then Adam said proudly, "This is our world, Eve. Ours to take care of. God said so. I heard her."

For a long time they sat there together in silence looking at the sea. After a while they became sleepy, so Adam took his wife tenderly in his arms and they slept under the stars.

On the seventh day, God rested. He
lay in his hammock under the trees and watched
Adam and Eve walking hand in hand in the
garden and the young animals playing together.
As he lay there, God felt a deep content: he had friends to help
him look after the world and all its creatures. He closed his eyes
and smiled, and thought about all the fun they would have together.

THE CREATION